Girl's Empowerment Activity Workbook

Created By: Dr. Jasmine Zapata

Dr. Zapata would like to send a special thank you and acknowledgment to all of the women and girls from across the U.S. who contributed quotes for the Beyond Beautiful Girls Empowerment book series over the years- some of which are included in this workbook.

This book is dedicated to all you powerful young ladies from around the world who are not afraid to let your light shine and who keep striving for greatness despite all that life may have thrown at you. You are Beyond Beautiful! You have everything inside of you needed to reach all of your goals. Keep holding your heads up.
Never give up!
We see you. We love you. YOU are enough.

"No one else in the world has the same exact combination of hair color, eye color, skin color, talents, knowledge, fears, passions, life experiences, dreams, or family members as

Y U"

-Dr. Jasmine Zapata

The Beyond Beautiful Declaration
By Dr. Jasmine Zapata

Today will be a great day!

I'll achieve all I set my mind to.

I cannot be stopped!

I can do anything I want to.

Cuz I'm Beyond Beautiful.

I'm BEYOND BEAUTIFUL.

I'm COURAGEOUS. I'm RESILIENT.

I'm CONFIDENT. I'm CREATIVE.

I am TALENTED, INTELLIGENT, UNIQUE, and INNOVATIVE!

I'm WORTH IT. I DESERVE IT.

I am TREASURED. I am LOVED.

I deserve every BLESSING

that is coming from ABOVE!

What makes a girl Beyond Beautiful?

List 10 things about yourself that make you Beyond Beautiful!

1. _____

2. _____

3. _____

4. _____

5. _____

6. _____

7. _____

8. _____

9. _____

10. _____

Introduce Yourself!

Name _____

Age _____   **Birthday** _____

Favorite Color _____

Favorite Food _____

Favorite Artist _____

Draw Yourself!

Draw yourself and somewhere on the page
write three things you love about yourself!

Beyond Beautiful Word Find

Find all the words that describe a girl who is Beyond Beautiful

```
N N I N M N C G F E N G V E
C O E K N N L E N F V E A U
E I M I N T E L L I G E N T
I B I N A A N N U G Z T N T
N R D D S P E C I A L A I N
N A R C R E A T I V E L M T
O V S T U N N I N G I G E A
V E T A L E N T E D G F M I
A V E S E N O A I L N T O E
T T U N T I E E I N S M S K
I I Q A L F I L O Z A Z E E
V I I T N E D I F N O C W B
E E N E S C N T D N C D A E
A V U I U C N P E T T E P R
```

Creative	Stunning	Brave
Innovative	Awesome	Confident
Talented	Intelligent	Special
Amazing	Kind	Unique

Beyond Beautiful

I AM WORTH IT
I DESERVE IT

BEYOND BEAUTIFUL™

Unique

Being unlike anything else

List 10 things about yourself that make you unique.

1. _____

2. _____

3. _____

4. _____

5. _____

6. _____

7. _____

8. _____

9. _____

10. _____

"Diamonds Do not start out with a Beautiful Appearance they have to go through A LOT to be formed"

-Dr. Jasmine Zapata

Journal

Use this page to write down your thoughts, feelings, or any positive messages you have for yourself!

_____

_____

_____

_____

_____

_____

_____

_____

_____

_____

_____

Good Vibes Only

BEYOND BEAUTIFUL™

Creating Goals

Write down 10 goals for yourself to complete this year. These could be anything from getting all A's in school to finding a new hobby!

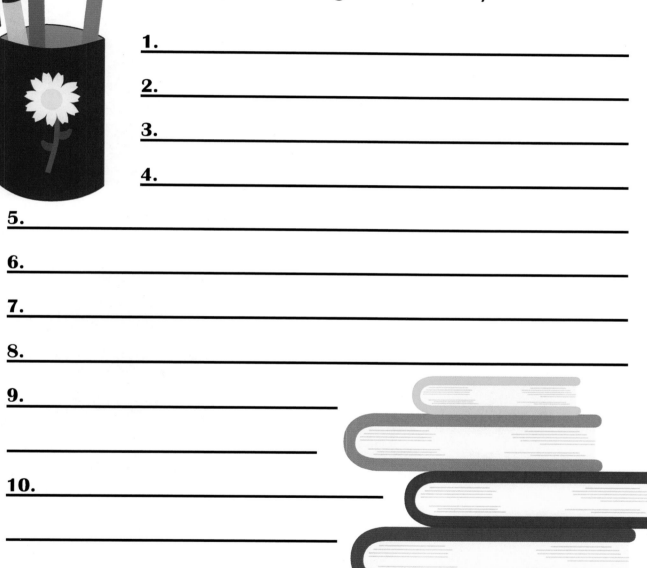

1. _____

2. _____

3. _____

4. _____

5. _____

6. _____

7. _____

8. _____

9. _____

_____

10. _____

_____

"If you believe in yourself and that you have something to contribute, you will be able to achieve your goals."
-Kaya Mondry

"What makes a girl Beyond Beautiful is her
PERSONALITY
and what she sets her
MIND TO
Not letting anyone decide for you.
Learning the right way to deal with things."

—Tamea Johnson

♥ Self-Love ♥

Caring about your own well-being and happiness

It may take a while for you to fully learn to love yourself, but if you are struggling, here is a place to start. Write down a few things about yourself that you love and would never want to change. This can be something on the inside or the outside!

1. _____

2. _____

3. _____

4. _____

5. _____

6. _____

7. _____

8. _____

9. _____

10. _____

LOVE ♥ YOURSELF

Draw a picture of you and your Best Friend

Creativity

Using your imagination

Part of expressing yourself is allowing yourself to be creative!
List a few places in your life where you express your creativity,
and fill this page with colors and drawings!

_____

_____

_____

_____

_____

_____

Doodle

Use this page to really express your creativity and fill it with colorful drawings and doodles!

Find A Quote!

Find a quote that inspires and uplifts you, then write it down
on this page and come back to it whenever you need it

_____

_____

_____

_____

_____

_____

_____

"Do not feed into negative energy, keep words of affirmations
around so you can remind yourself of your worth."
-Brandi Rimmer

 **23**

6 Tips for Better Studying

1. Study with Friends

Studying with friends can make things more fun, and they can help you stay focused!

2. Be Creative

Come up with creative activities or other ways to help you remember information, like a song for memorizing vocab words!

3. Flashcards

Flashcards are a great way to help you stay focused and cover everything you need to study!

"Remember your end goal to keep you motivated"
-Cameo Hazlewood

4. Take Breaks
The best way to stay focused and relaxed while studying is to take breaks every hour.

5. Snacks!
Getting hungry while studying can be very distracting so make sure you have a healthy snack on hand to keep you fueled up!

6. Drink Water
You do not want to get dehydrated, so make sure you have a bottle of water nearby to keep you happy and healthy.

Journal

Use this page to write down your thoughts or feelings.
You can also write more ways you want to express your
creativity or ideas you have for better studying!

_____

_____

_____

_____

_____

_____

_____

_____

_____

_____

_____

BEYOND BEAUTIFUL™

Self-Esteem

Confidence in your worth and abilities

Write 10 ways you can boost your self-esteem. These could be daily words of affirmation you say to yourself like "I am beautiful!" or "I am worth it!" It could also be goals you would like to reach like dressing the way you want!

1. _____

2. _____

3. _____

4. _____

5. _____

6. _____

7. _____

8. _____

9. _____

10. _____

Killing IT!

"Never lose faith in love, in humanity, and most importantly, in yourself."
-Sanskruti Kakaria

Use every situation as an opportunity to LEARN and GROW

–Trenika Williams

BEYOND BEAUTIFUL™

Innovation

Imagining new methods and ideas

Write a few ways that you can be more innovative and creative in your everyday life!

1. _____

_____

2. _____

_____

3. _____

_____

4. _____

_____

REACH FOR THE STARS

What are You Thankful For?

List a few things that you are most thankful for in life and then draw them out!

1. _____

2. _____

3. _____

4. _____

5. _____

"I found it helpful to keep a gratitude list, and a list of accomplishments (both personal and professional) that helped me whenever I needed a confidence boost." -Varuska Patni

  BEYOND BEAUTIFUL™

Dreams and Aspirations

Write down your dreams in life and what goals you aspire to reach! These could be anything from future career goals to building your self-confidence or standing up for yourself.

1. _____

2. _____

3. _____

4. _____

5. _____

6. _____

7. _____

8. _____

9. _____

10. _____

"Get to know yourself by figuring out your passion and growing comfortable in your skin."
-Logan Dean

Create a Mantra

Come up with a positive phrase that builds you up and write it down all over this page! Repeat this phrase to yourself whenever you need motivation or to reassure yourself of your purpose!

Self-Care Tips:

"Self-care is setting firm and healthy boundaries, protecting your peace, and avoiding unhealthy environments or situations." -Latricia Pitts

Schedule Time to Relax

School, work, and your social life can get stressful! Try to schedule in some relaxation time at some point in your day so you can take a breath and recharge.

Start Each Day With Something Good

Dressing in an outfit that makes you feel confident or having a favorite breakfast can put you in a good mood at the start of every day!

Find Hobbies That Make You Happy

Having an activity to do during your free time that brings you pleasure can be a great way to bring joy into your everyday life!

BEYOND BEAUTIFUL

At the End of Every Day, Write Down Five Good Things That Happened

Sometimes it's easy to focus only on the negative parts of your day. This tip can help you recognize the positive moments of every day, no matter how small!

Get rid of Negative People

Sometimes you will have people in your life who claim to be your friends, but only tear you down. It is okay to cut these people out of your life! It may be hard, but a real friend will encourage you, not make you feel bad about yourself.

Drink Water!

Staying hydrated is super important for a healthy lifestyle and it can sometimes help with your mood!

"There are going to be tough times, hard times, scary times, and bad times—but there is always a light at the end of the tunnel."
-Minyona Mason

Managing Negative thoughts and Feelings

Sometimes it is easy to get caught up in the negatives. Here are a few tips to help you focus on the positives instead.

1. Focus on your strengths! Remember all the things you are good at!

2. Remember that sadness is temporary. Things may feel difficult now, but they always get better.

3. Allow yourself to feel your feelings. Do not try and shut them down or tell yourself that you should not be feeling that way.

4. Tell someone you trust. Sometimes just talking about your feelings helps you to understand them and manage them better.

Fill the rest of the spaces with other ways you can be more positive in your daily life.

1. _____

2. _____

3. _____

4. _____

5. _____

BEYOND BEAUTIFUL™

"You are NOT Other People's opinions. You are NOT Other People's expectations."

—Kayla Thomas

BEYOND BEAUTIFUL™

Journal

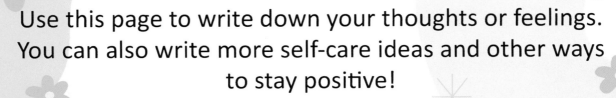

Use this page to write down your thoughts or feelings. You can also write more self-care ideas and other ways to stay positive!

_____

_____

_____

_____

_____

_____

_____

_____

_____

_____

Favorite Memory

Draw a memory that brings you joy and that you never want to forget!

Courage

The ability to face difficulty without fear

Write about a moment in your life that took a lot of courage to get through.

_____

_____

_____

_____

_____

_____

_____

_____

_____

_____

"Beyond Beautiful means to cherish your flaws whether external or internal and to know that no one can love you or appreciate your beauty more than you do".

–Kenyatta Young

Overcoming Obstacles

Everyone experiences hardships at some point in their life. Write down a few moments where you were going through a hard time but you overcame it!

1. _____

2. _____

3. _____

4. _____

5. _____

6. _____

7. _____

8. _____

9. _____

10. _____

"If you have faith that you can get through it, you will."
-Lalebela Moore

Draw a Role Model

Draw someone who you look up to! This should be someone who uplifts and inspires you. Then, write down a few lessons they have taught you.

Collage

Cover this whole page spread with a collage of your favorite things! Cut out pictures from magazines, tape in photos of your friends, and fill the pages with color!

BEYOND BEAUTIFUL™

Anxiety

Worry and fear about everyday situations

It is normal to experience anxiety, especially as you get older. Write down a few things that make you anxious. Then, write some ways you can try to overcome that anxiety!

1. _____

_____

2. _____

_____

3. _____

_____

4. _____

_____

5. _____

_____

_____

BEYOND BEAUTIFUL™

"Remind yourself that you have a PURPOSE"

-Taylor E. Melville

BEYOND BEAUTIFUL™

Resilience

The ability to recover from difficulties and tough situations

We all go through situations that test us. Being able to recover from hard times and come back even stronger is a great trait to work on. Write down any difficult situations you have been through and how you came back from them.

1. _____

_____

2. _____

_____

3. _____

_____

4. _____

_____

5. _____

_____

BEYOND BEAUTIFUL™

"Big things don't come easy, but you have CONTROL and POWER over each day."

- Jade O. Norman

Journal

Use this page to write down your thoughts, feelings, or any other reflections you have.

_____

_____

_____

_____

_____

_____

_____

_____

_____

_____

_____

_____

BEYOND BEAUTIFUL™

Take this page to
PAUSE
and just...
BREATHE

BEYOND BEAUTIFUL™

Persistence

Not giving up, even during tough times

Write a few things that you do or can do to help you stay persistent even during difficult times.

1. _____

_____

2. _____

_____

3. _____

_____

4. _____

_____

5. _____

_____

"Oftentimes we are our number one critic, but it's important to remember that we are a work in progress and that we only learn to grow from making mistakes and failure."
-Jacqueline Zuniga Paiz

BEYOND BEAUTIFUL™

"**Beyond Beautiful**
means to
RESPECT
YOURSELF
and to
FOLLOW YOUR
OWN
PATH"

-Nevaeh Thompson

 **53**

Aspiration

The hope of achieving something

Write down 10 things that you aspire to achieve by the end of the year!

1. _____

2. _____

3. _____

4. _____

5. _____

6. _____

7. _____

8. _____

9. _____

10. _____

"Never stop dreaming, there is always so much to do for you to become who you are meant to be and make the world a better place!" -Aleeya Conway

"Your age, gender, race, social class, or anything else people try to label you with, is not a determinant of what you can and will achieve."

—Aliyah Gillespie

Your Future

Imagine what your life will be like in 10 years and use this page to draw it out!

BEYOND BEAUTIFUL™

Now use this page to list a few things you can do this year to make those dreams a reality!

1. _____

_____

2. _____

_____

3. _____

_____

4. _____

_____

5. _____

_____

_____

"You are capable. You Matter. Your presence is a gift to the world."
-Latricia Pitts

Passion

Intense desire and enthusiasm

List five things that you are passionate about and explain why you are passionate about those things!

1. _____

_____

2. _____

_____

3. _____

_____

4. _____

_____

5. _____

_____

_____

"Your path may not look like everyone else's, but you will achieve your goals. Embrace the journey."
-Trenika J. Williams

"What makes a girl Beyond Beautiful is her spirit. Her spirit. Her spirit! It's how she treats her family. How she treats herself. The way she carries herself, especially in the midst of a trial."

–Roylene Gracelia Johnson

Use this page to write down a few ways that you can follow Roylene Gracelia Johnson's advice on what makes a girl Beyond Beautiful

1. _____

_____

2. _____

_____

3. _____

_____

4. _____

_____

5. _____

_____

Always Stay POSITIVE

"Beyond Beautiful is our capacity to LOVE. To love not only ourselves, but also our fellow man. Being Beyond Beautiful goes so much deeper than surface level appearances, popularity, makeup, clothing, or socioeconomic status. Learning to love ourselves and others is a life long journey of self-reflection, empathy, acceptance, and forgiveness. Beyond Beautiful is about building up and not tearing down. It is about being patient with ourselves and with others. It is about striving to be the best "me" that I can be. It is about going forward and not looking back. Just as a single snowflake falls from the sky, uniquely different than all the rest, so each of us is divinely fashioned to be Beyond Beautiful in our own special way."

-Julia Grace Saffold

Beyond Beautiful™

Made in the USA
Columbia, SC
25 March 2022

58115287R00035